CGP

True Tales

of

Scientists

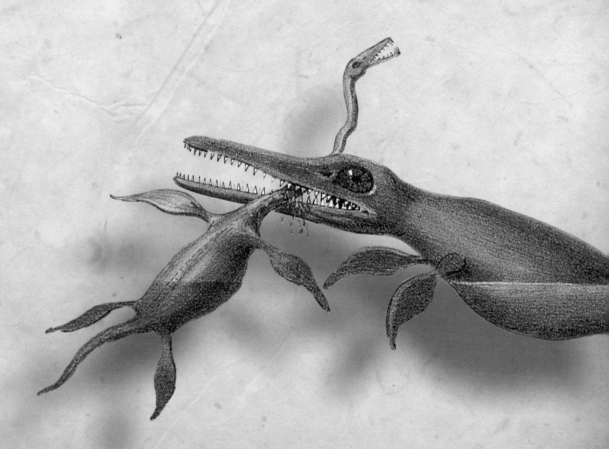

Credits

Editors: Claire Boulter, Paul Jordin, Anthony Muller, Rebecca Tate

Consultant: Rachel Clark

With thanks to Anthony Muller, Holly Poynton, Glenn Rogers, Camilla Simson, Karen Wells, Janet Berkeley, Alison Griffin, Judy Hornigold and Maxine Petrie for the proofreading.

With thanks to Laura Jakubowski for the copyright research.

With thanks to John Kitching for the design work.

Published by CGP

ISBN: 978 1 84762 477 2

Printed by Elanders Ltd, Newcastle upon Tyne.

Contents

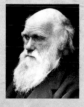

© The Natural History Museum / Alamy

© Photos.com/Thinkstock

Acknowledgements

Image on cover and introduction page © Oxford University Museum of Natural History, UK / Bridgeman Images

Image on contents page and page 1: Image of Ibn al-Haytham by Wronkiew licenced for re-use under the creative commons licence http://creativecommons.org/licenses/by-sa/3.0/

Image on page 1: Bust of Aristotle, photographer Jastrow (2006), Ludovisi Collection.

Image on page 12: Model of a "Persian Windmill" in the German Museum, Munich photographer Saupreiß licenced for re-use under the creative commons licence http://creativecommons.org/licenses/by-sa/3.0/deed.en

Image on page 12: Wall tiling at the Alhambra by Dmharvey licenced for re-use under the creative commons licence http://creativecommons.org/licenses/by/3.0/deed.en

Image on page 16: Drawing of the skull of Temnodontosaurus - Everard Home (1756 - 1832)

Image on page 18: Belemnite by Obsidian Soul, licenced for re-use under the creative commons licence http://creativecommons.org/licenses/by/3.0/deed.en

Image of plesiosaur fossil on page 22: Lithograph of Plesiosaurus dolichodeirus skeleton found by Mary Anning in 1823, published in 1824 transactions of the Geological Society of London.

Image of plesiosaur painting on page 22: Plesiosaur by Heinrich Harder

Image on page 27: 'Charles Darwin' Down House, Downe, Kent, UK / © English Heritage Photo Library / Bridgeman Images

Image on page 28: 'Charles Darwin' Down House, Downe, Kent, UK / © English Heritage Photo Library / Bridgeman Images

Image on page 31: 'Emma Darwin' Down House, Downe, Kent, UK / © English Heritage Photo Library / Bridgeman Images

Image of horse fossils on page 32: Universal History Archive/UIG /Bridgeman Images

Image on page 32: Portrait de Jean-Baptiste Lamarck. 1893.

Image on page 35: Charles & William Darwin 1842.

Image on page 35: B990676.tif - Photograph of Annie Darwin © English Heritage

Image on page 36: 'The Origin of the Species', Natural History Museum, London, UK / The Bridgeman Images

Image on page 37: 'Darwin in his study' Down House, Downe, Kent, UK / © English Heritage Photo Library / Bridgeman Images

Image on contents page and page 39: Charles Darwin Photo by J. Cameron, 1869

Image on page 44: Uraninite image by Rob Lavinsky, iRocks.com – CC-BY-SA-3.0 licenced for re-use under the creative commons licence http://creativecommons.org/licenses/by/3.0/deed.en

Image on page 47: The Curie Pavillion at the Radium Institute in 1925 © Musée Curie (coll. ACJC).

With thanks to Alamy, CGTextures.com, Clipart.com, iStockphoto.com, Science Photo Library and Thinkstockphotos.co.uk for permission to use the stock images in this book.

Alhazen

"A man of vision"

written by Paul Jordin

MARCH 979 Alhazen (Al-ha-zan) raced through the crowded streets of **Basra**. He was going to be late again! The market was as busy as ever, full of traders from far and wide haggling with their customers. Lungs bursting, Alhazen sped across the square towards the school building that was attached to the **mosque**. At the door to the classroom, he almost crashed into his teacher.

Alhazen lived from 965 to around 1040. He is also known as Ibn al-Haytham (Ib-en al-Hi-thum).

"Cutting things fine again, I see," the teacher said with a shake of his head. "What kept you this time?"

Alhazen looked sheepish. "I got distracted watching the shadows of the city walls. Did you know, if you watch really closely, you can actually see the shadows getting shorter?"

The teacher scoffed. "Watching shadows! Why does your father hire tutors who fill your head with such nonsense? Remember, your studies here at the **maktab** must come first. Your religious education will bring you closer to God."

Out of respect, Alhazen held his tongue. The teachers at the maktab spoke a lot about God, but Alhazen already knew he wanted to get closer to God by studying the world He created instead of just listening to what other people had to say about Him.

*Alhazen was inspired by the **philosopher** and scientist Aristotle (Ar-iss-tot-ull), who learned as much as he could by examining the world around him.*

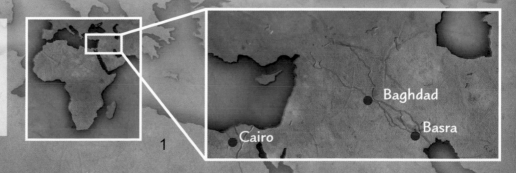

This map shows some of the places Alhazen lived. Today, Cairo is the capital city of Egypt, and Basra and Baghdad are in Iraq.

Baghdad

Basra

Cairo

1

The House of Wisdom

Modern-day Baghdad is the capital city of Iraq. Not much of the Baghdad Alhazen knew has survived. Most of the oldest part of the city was destroyed by invaders in 1258.

JANUARY 991 Spreading out for many miles either side of the River Tigris (Ty-griss), Baghdad was the largest city in the world. Walking through the streets of the city, Alhazen shook his head, turning to his friend. "I thought Basra was crowded," he said, "but Baghdad is something else. I still can't get used to the size of this place!"

His friend laughed. "That's because you hardly spend any time in the real city! You're always indoors studying. You know, it wouldn't do you any harm to have a bit of fun now and again!"

Alhazen was used to his friend's teasing. He had to admit it was true: he did spend most of his days in the House of Wisdom. But what was wrong with that? The House of Wisdom was the reason he'd come to live in Baghdad in the first place. Surely there was no greater library in the world! Alhazen made his living there, translating important works by great thinkers into Arabic, so anyone could read them.

However, it wasn't really fair to say that he spent all his time indoors. Alhazen knew it was his duty as a scientist to study the real world whenever he could. Lately, he'd developed an interest in **astronomy**, and had taken to making trips to the **observatory** in the hills beyond the city.

Ptolemy lived 900 years before Alhazen. As an expert in the same subjects, Alhazen was later nicknamed 'Ptolemy the Second', but he wasn't afraid to criticise his hero. He wrote an entire book explaining why some of Ptolemy's ideas were wrong.

There, with access to accurate instruments and clear desert skies, Alhazen could track the movements of the stars and planets. He'd been studying the works of the great mathematician and astronomer Ptolemy (Tol-em-ee) and wanted to compare his own observations with the ones Ptolemy had recorded.

2

Alhazen turned to his friend. "So, I don't get out enough, eh? How about this — I'll spend today with you in the city if you join me at the observatory tomorrow night. I'll even teach you how to stargaze..."

How to Draw a Star Map

You don't need any special equipment to go stargazing. To make your own star map, all you need is a sheet of paper, a pencil, a compass and a clear night sky.

1. Draw a large circle on your sheet of paper. Using your compass, find which direction is north and mark it at the top of your circle.

2. Mark points around the edge of the circle for east, south and west. Watch out — on a star map, east and west are swapped round from where they are on a normal map, because a star map shows the sky as you look away from the Earth. (If you hold your map up to the sky, with north on the map pointing to north in real life, you'll see that all the other compass directions will point the correct way.)

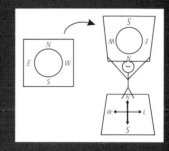

3. Look for landmarks on the horizon. Draw some of them in the correct places at the edge of the circle. They'll make it easier to match bits of the sky to bits of your map.

4. Draw dots on your circle to show where the stars are. Start with the stars directly above you — they go in the centre of the circle.

5. Add the stars you can see in the rest of the sky. Use bigger dots to show brighter stars. If the moon is out, add it to the map too.

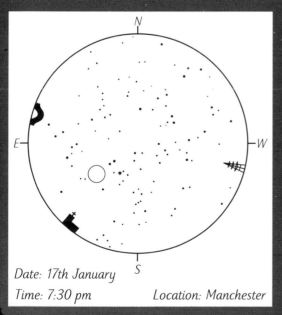

Date: 17th January
Time: 7:30 pm   Location: Manchester

6. Don't forget to write down the date, time and location for your map.

7. Compare your star map against books and maps that other astronomers have made. See if you can identify the stars and **constellations** you saw.

Nightmare on the Nile

MAY 1011 Alhazen was in high spirits as he rode out of **Cairo** — just as he had been since he arrived in Egypt a few days earlier. He'd been summoned there by the country's ruler, **Caliph** (Cal-eef) al-Hakim (al Ha-keem). Although he was only twenty-five years old, al-Hakim was one of the most powerful men in the world and had already ruled Egypt for more than ten years. In that time his support for **scholars** and his love of learning had become almost as well known as his unpredictable temper.

Somehow, al-Hakim had heard about Alhazen's ideas for controlling the mighty River Nile. Alhazen thought it was possible to tame the Nile by building a huge dam to control the river's flooding and save the water for times of drought. He had never dreamt he'd get the chance to put his plan into action, but that was exactly what al-Hakim wanted him to do. Alhazen knew it would have been unwise to turn the Caliph down, even if he'd wanted to. Only a fool would risk upsetting the 'Mad Caliph'.

Al-Hakim ruled an empire stretching across parts of North Africa and the Middle East. Historians disagree on whether or not he really deserved to be known as the 'Mad Caliph'.

JUNE 1011 As his journey continued over the following weeks, Alhazen's excitement began to give way to anxiety. The river wasn't narrowing as much as he expected it to. Worse still, the shape of the valley it flowed through was nothing like he'd imagined. As he took more observations and measurements, a feeling of dread crept over him like a cloud blocking out the sun. His calculations weren't just slightly out — the dam would have to be hundreds of metres wider than he'd thought. Alhazen had taken on an impossible task for a man who did not like to be disappointed. Now he knew he might have to pay for his failure with his life...

The River Nile as it might have looked in Alhazen's day.

A Desperate Gamble

JULY 1011 Half a day's ride from Cairo, Alhazen was the last person awake in the camp. He'd stayed up to watch the sunset, knowing it might be the last one he'd ever see. Now, night had fallen and he was unable to sleep. Feeling it was pointless to just lie awake, he started writing a letter to a friend in Baghdad.

My friend,

I have so much to tell you. The task I was set here in Egypt, which I so foolishly promised I could complete, has turned out to be impossible!

I remember how we joked before I left for Egypt about al-Hakim — the 'Mad Caliph' — but those tall tales about his strange laws are true. I heard that he had all the dogs in Cairo killed because their barking annoyed him. And he really does make the shops open all night and close during the day.

When I realised I couldn't deliver what he'd asked of me, suddenly al-Hakim's odd behaviour didn't seem so funny. Everyone here lives in fear of upsetting him, for al-Hakim thinks nothing of having even his closest advisors put to death when they displease him. Surely I will suffer the same fate.

I have but one chance. It's clear to me now that I must have been mad to take on such a task for such a man. So, mad I shall be! I'll go before al-Hakim tomorrow with wild hair, and wilder eyes, to try to convince him I've gone insane. Perhaps he'll show mercy to a madman...

THE NEXT DAY Alhazen looked this way and that, swatting at invisible insects, leaping on tables, and, above all, avoiding eye contact with the Caliph. He'd ranted and raved about the desert heat and the wild, untameable river. He'd pretended not to understand the questions he'd been asked. He'd pulled at his straggly hair and torn clothes, still stained with mud from the banks of the Nile. He'd greeted statues as if they were old friends. At one point, he'd even performed an impression of a crocodile.

Now, as he waited to see if the Caliph believed him, Alhazen's heart thumped in his chest and a trickle of sweat ran down his brow. Al-Hakim watched the scholar intently. Then, slowly and deliberately, he stood up, ready to deliver his judgment...

Alone with his Thoughts

SEPTEMBER 1011 It was another hot, dusty day in Cairo. For the third time that morning, Aziz tried to ignore the voice coming through the door behind him.

"Please! Please, I know you can hear me! I need —"

"Quiet!" Aziz snapped. "You've already had your food and water for today."

"I don't want food; it's much more important than that," hissed the prisoner.
"Paper! Ink! A pen! I must be able to write!" Aziz shook his head and smiled to himself. The man was under **house arrest**, and all he could do was fuss about paper and pens? He really must be crazy.

OCTOBER 1011 Alhazen sat up with a start as the door opened unexpectedly.
Aziz thrust the small bundle of writing materials into the prisoner's hands.

"Here, if it'll keep you quiet, take these," the guard muttered. "But you didn't get them from me, right?" And with that, he was gone.

"Thank you! Thank you so much!" Alhazen called after him. Paper, a simple pen and a small bottle of ink! Finally he would be able to write down some of the thoughts and ideas that had been racing through his head. Al-Hakim could lock him up and take away his books, but Alhazen still had his mind — and that was the most important thing of all.

THREE WEEKS LATER Aziz bowed theatrically as he handed over a fresh delivery of paper. "And is there anything else I can fetch for you, sir?" he asked.

"Actually," Alhazen replied, ignoring the guard's sarcasm, "perhaps you could find me one or two bits and pieces. I want to test some of my ideas. I'll need a long, narrow tube of some sort, and a mirror if you can find one. Candles too — at least a couple, but three or four would be better..."

Aziz sighed and rolled his eyes. What had he got himself into?

6

Lighting the Way

APRIL 1015 Aziz shivered in the night air and looked down at the five candles. He'd lined them up outside Alhazen's home, carefully following the prisoner's instructions. Inside, Alhazen sat in the dark and waited. The window next to him was completely covered with thick, dark cloth, except for a tiny hole in the middle of the material. Aziz carefully lit each candle, and as he did so, Alhazen watched five points of light appear on the wall opposite.

Alhazen is sometimes called the 'father of the scientific method'. The scientific method means coming up with ideas and testing them with experiments. The results of the experiments either help to prove the ideas, or help show when they're wrong. This is what all modern scientists do, but Alhazen was one of the first to work like this.

Alhazen gave a low whistle: the signal for Aziz to start the next part of the experiment. Aziz held a board between the first candle and the window, and, inside the house, Alhazen saw one of the spots of light vanish. A count of ten later, and it reappeared as Aziz removed the board. Aziz moved along the line of candles, repeating the same action for each one.

A short while later, Aziz opened the door. "How was that? Did anything happen?"

"Oh yes, my friend," the scientist replied, "it certainly did! The lights on the wall disappeared one by one as you blocked the light from each candle, just as I predicted. That proves that each of these lights matches up to one of the candles."

"The rays of light from the candles pass through this hole together," he said, pointing to the cloth over the window, "but there are still five separate lights on the wall. This shows that rays of light from different objects can cross without getting mixed up — *and* I've proved it with an experiment so simple anyone could repeat it! If only I weren't stuck in here, then I could let the whole world know!"

Challenging the Ancients

AUGUST 1016 Alhazen's light experiments had given him some interesting new ideas about how eyesight worked. He'd read all the old books on the subject, but nothing in them quite seemed to fit. Before his house arrest, he'd often debated new ideas with other scholars, and he still missed being able to do this. Instead, he took a fresh sheet of paper and tried to gather his thoughts.

There have been different suggestions through the centuries about how eyesight works, but I find them all unsatisfactory. The great thinkers of the past have much to teach us, but we mustn't assume everything they wrote is true.

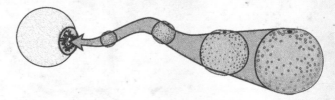

Some ancients believed that when you look at an object, it releases a sort of skin, or a copy of itself, which enters the eye.

However, that can't be true. If it were, surely you would be able to see the whole object, even if part of it was hidden behind something else. Added to this, many objects are much bigger than your eye. How could their 'skins' be small enough to get into the eye?

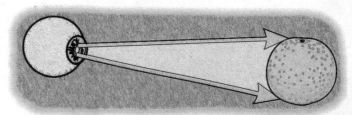

On the other hand, some argue that beams of light come out of your eyes. They say that when you look at an object, these beams scan it so you can see it.

This can't be true either. If the light I see with comes from my own eyes, I would be able to see in the dark. In addition, it hurts your eyes to look at bright things, like the sun. In other words, the evidence suggests that the light is coming into the eye, not going out of it.

In conclusion, it's clear to me that nobody has come up with an idea that fully explains how people see. Some parts of the old ideas make sense, but there are parts of each explanation that can't be true. For example, information must come from the object to the eye, but not in the form of a 'skin'. And while it's true that beams of light travel in straight lines, they can't come out of the eye. Perhaps the true explanation combines parts of the old ideas in a new way.

A Change of Fortune

FEBRUARY 1021 Alhazen could tell something strange was going on. There had been some sort of commotion in the early hours of the morning, but by the afternoon an eerie hush had fallen over the city. It wasn't until Aziz arrived for evening guard duty that Alhazen finally got an explanation.

"Caliph al-Hakim is missing!" he exclaimed. "He rode out into the hills last night, as he often does, but this time he didn't return. This afternoon, they found his donkey and some of his clothes, which were all torn and bloodstained — but of the Caliph himself, there was no trace!"

"Some people are saying he grew bored of his responsibilities and fled the kingdom. His most faithful followers — those who claim he's God in human form — believe he has returned to heaven. There are darker rumours, too. Some say the Caliph's sister, Sitt al-Mulk, arranged to have him murdered! The Caliph's son, Ali az-Zahir (az-Za-heer), is too young to rule on his own, so Sitt al-Mulk will take charge of the kingdom for now. Hopefully they'll rule more fairly than al-Hakim did..."

MARCH 1021 "Well," began the government official, "I'm sorry it's taken a couple of weeks for anyone to come around here. As I'm sure you can imagine, things have been rather busy since the Caliph's disappearance."

Alhazen laughed nervously. "Of course," he replied. He thought he knew why the man was here, but he hardly dared believe it. Was this the moment he'd waited so long for?

"Don't look so nervous," smiled the official. "I'm here to inform you that the order to keep you under house arrest has been lifted. You are a free man! I have been instructed to pass on the new Caliph's apologies for your treatment. He hopes that you'll remain in Cairo — but of your own free will this time! There would be a teaching job available for you at al-Azhar University, if you chose to stay..."

Al-Azhar Mosque and University still stands today. Alhazen worked there after he was released.

© B.O'Kane / Alamy

9

A Musical Experiment

JUNE 1029 A small crowd stood in the shade at one end of the courtyard. There were a few of Alhazen's students and fellow scholars, a group of traders, and some ordinary citizens hoping for some entertainment. The Cairo locals had all heard of Alhazen and his experiments, but today's promised to be something a bit different.

One of the traders had been taking instructions from Alhazen. Now, the crowd watched with growing curiosity as the trader mounted his camel and Alhazen handed him a small flute.

At times like this, Aziz wondered why he'd left the Caliph's service to work for Alhazen. "Surely music is a human idea," he frowned. "It can't have any effect on animals!"

"We can't know that until we investigate," Alhazen replied. "After all these years as my assistant, you know my methods. I think animals *do* respond to music, but I need to carry out experiments to see if I'm right."

Alhazen called out to the nervous-looking trader. "Please, start when you're ready!" The man clicked an instruction to his camel and, guided by its rider, the animal began walking around the circuit Aziz had marked out around the edge of the courtyard.

By early afternoon, Alhazen had recorded the camel's times for many laps. Some had been with the rider playing no music, some while he played fast music, and some with a gentler rhythm. He looked over the results and smiled with satisfaction.

"You see," he said, "what did I tell you? The camel sped up when it heard fast music, and slowed down for the slower music!"

"And are we done with camels now?" Aziz sighed.

"Yes, for the time being," Alhazen replied as they left the courtyard. "Tomorrow — horses!"

A Scientific Legacy

AUGUST 1039 Aziz was sorting through Alhazen's post for him. "Ah, here's an interesting one," he said. "One of your former students is now living in Basra. He's invited you to visit him. Fancy another trip back to your home town?"

Alhazen shook his head. "No, my travelling days are done," he said. "I said my goodbyes to Basra last time we were there. I'll see out what little time I have left here in Cairo." Seeing the look on his friend's face, he continued, "Don't be sad for me. Look around you."

Alhazen indicated the shelves that lined his study. On one wall were the books he'd studied, written by great men of the past such as Aristotle and Ptolemy. Opposite them were Alhazen's own works — dozens of books, covering subjects including astronomy, mathematics, light and vision. In pride of place was his seven-volume *Book of Optics*. This book, which Alhazen had started writing while under house arrest, described his experiments and ideas to do with light and eyesight.

"I am an old man, and my work in this world is almost done. But look at what I will leave behind. I hope that future scientists will not only read my books, but follow my methods too. And that means they should challenge my works, find my mistakes and try to improve on my ideas, just as I did with those who came before me."

> ***"...the duty of the man who investigates the writings of scientists ... is to make himself an enemy of all that he reads, and ... attack it from every side."***

IN LATER CENTURIES Alhazen got his wish. His most important books were translated into many languages. Later scientists read and improved on the work Alhazen did in the *Book of Optics*.

All scientists today share Alhazen's focus on using evidence from experiments to back up their ideas. In this way, he continues to influence the work of every new generation of scientists.

Today, Alhazen's face appears on banknotes and stamps, and everything from university buildings to a moon crater have been named after him.

A Golden Age

Alhazen was one of many wise men of the Islamic Golden Age. This was a period between the 7th and 13th centuries when many great thinkers were at work in countries with Muslim rulers. Here are just a few examples of their achievements:

Inventions

Muslim inventors were full of bright ideas for clever contraptions. They created early versions of everything from windmills to gliders to fountain pens. They also found new and improved ways of making a whole range of useful things including soap, gunpowder, pottery and perfume.

Model of a medieval Persian windmill

Medieval Muslim astronomers

Astronomy

Medieval Muslim astronomers carefully studied and recorded the movements of the planets and stars. They translated and updated earlier books by Greek and Indian astronomers. They also made improvements to the instruments used for astronomy, making them much more accurate.

Art and Architecture

Muslim **architects** created many stunning buildings. They were often decorated with patterns of repeated shapes — this style of decoration is now known as 'arabesque'. Artists painted beautiful illustrations for books, while others made decorative glassware, metalwork, pottery and fabrics.

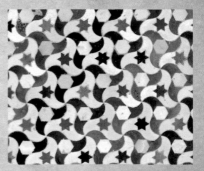

An arabesque tile pattern

© SHEILA TERRY/SCIENCE PHOTO LIBRARY

A painting of the famous Muslim doctor Abulcasis (Ab-ool-cass-iss)

Medicine

Many medical advances were made by early Muslim doctors. Some of their books were used to teach medicine for hundreds of years. They invented new treatments and medical tools, studied the causes of diseases and improved understanding of how the human body works.

Glossary

architects — People who design buildings

astronomy — The study of the stars, planets and space

Basra — A city in modern-day Iraq and the birthplace of Alhazen

Cairo — The capital city of modern-day Egypt

Caliph — A title used for political or religious leaders in some Muslim countries

constellations — Named groups of stars

house arrest — A punishment where a prisoner is locked up in their own home instead of being sent to prison

maktab — An Islamic school, usually attached to a mosque

mosque — A Muslim place of worship

observatory — A building used for studying the stars and planets

philosopher — A person who aims to understand the world using logic and reasoning

scholars — Well-educated people who are experts in one or more subjects

Mary Anning

"Fossil Hunter"

written by Rebecca Tate

NOVEMBER 1809 Ten-year-old Mary skipped along the beach, trying to keep up with her father. The winter wind bit savagely through her ragged dress, but she barely noticed the chill.

The previous night she had lain awake, listening to the waves crashing against the cliffs. She had guessed that there might be a landslide overnight, which would expose some new curiosities, and she was right.

Suddenly she spotted a dark outline in the soft stone of the cliff.

"Pa!" she shouted excitedly, "I've found somethin'!"

Her father rushed over to her.

*Mary lived in Lyme Regis, on the south coast of England. It has cliffs full of **fossils**, which local people called curiosities.*

"It's a stone fish," he said as he scraped away the crumbling stone to reveal its beauty. "We're sure to get a good price for it. Good work, my little Mary."

LATER THAT DAY, Mary sat watching her father intently. He was teaching her how to make her fossil fish ready to sell.

First, he showed her how to use a brush to carefully remove the dry dust from the delicate fossil. Then he picked up a sharp metal pin. Using the most precise of movements, he began to scrape away the last of the rock from the tiny gaps between the bones of the stone fish.

"It's your turn now," he said, handing her the pin.

Gingerly, Mary began to copy her father's movements.

A fossil fish.

14

An Ocean of Tears

A YEAR LATER Mary stood in front of her father's freshly dug grave, her cheeks wet with tears. Waves of grief washed over her as she said her final farewell to the man who had encouraged her love of the beach and of all the wonderful things they found there.

Mary couldn't imagine going out to collect curiosities without her father. Who would tell her the names of the things she found? Who would carry her over the rocks if they were too slippery? Who would keep her company while she cleaned her finds?

As well as being devastated by grief, the family had lost their main source of income — her father's business. They had no money to buy food, let alone wood for the fire. With winter tightening its grip, Mary knew her mother would have to ask for money from the church. It broke her heart to see her proud, determined mother forced to beg. There must be something she could do to help!

Mary's father made furniture. This didn't make much money, so Mary's family was poor even before he died.

THE NEXT DAY Mary wandered forlornly away from the stony beach, clutching the precious curiosity she had found there. She would keep it to remember her father by.

In town, she passed a group of ladies in fine gowns and elegant bonnets. One of them called out to her: "What did you find on the beach? May we see it?"

Reluctantly, Mary handed the snakestone to the lady.

"I'll give you half a crown for it," the lady stated, already drawing the coin from her purse.

Mary was too stunned to argue. Half a crown would feed her family for a week. Could this be the answer to her family's money worries? Her father had sold the curiosities he found — she would do the same!

A snakestone was what we now call an ammonite (am-o-night). It's a fossil of a sea creature with a spiral shell.

15

Treasures of the Earth

FEBRUARY 1812 Mary heaved the bag of fossils onto her back and picked up her hammer, ready to head home. As she turned to go, something strange caught her eye. Sticking out of the cliff in a neat row were three dark stones, each about the size of her fist. Using her hammer, she chipped gently at the rock surrounding the strange stones — there were more of them underneath!

We now know that the skull was from an ichthyosaur (ik-thee-o-sore) — a large, swimming reptile that looked a bit like a dolphin.

As she worked, Mary's heart began to beat faster. Six months ago, her brother, Joseph, had burst into the house shouting that he'd found something amazing. It was an enormous skull, over a metre long and different from any creature either of them had seen before. Joseph was busy at work, so he told Mary where he had found the skull and asked her to look for the rest of the skeleton. Had she finally found it?

Mary chipped away at the cliff until the sun was low in the sky and the tide threatened to block her way home. Reluctantly, she stopped work, vowing to return at dawn.

JULY 1812 Mary's hands shook as she swept the last of the dust from the huge fossil. It had taken her months of painstaking work to uncover the skeleton embedded in the cliff. A team of men had helped her break the immense slab of stone containing the entire fossil out of the cliff and carry it to her workshop. There, she had needed all of her skill and patience to carefully scrape away the rest of the surrounding rock without damaging the ancient fossil. All she had left to do was polish the fossil and use plaster to fix it into the wooden frame her brother had built.

Mary stood back and peered through the settling dust at the fossilised bones of the huge, mysterious creature once more. What could it be?

A drawing of the fossilised skull found by Joseph Anning.

OCTOBER 1813 Mary ran upstairs and flew over to her table, clutching her new book. In all of her fourteen years, she had never owned a book — until today. Her generous neighbour, Mrs. Stock, had given her a beautiful one, all about **geology**. Perhaps it would tell her more about the strange creature she and Joseph had chipped from the cliff. She gently stroked the smooth leather of the cover, opened it, and began to read.

An Introduction to Fossils

In some parts of the world, strange stones that look like bones, animals or plants can be found. These stones are called fossils.

What are fossils?

Fossils are the remains of living things that have been preserved in rock over extremely long periods of time. The animals and plants that are preserved often don't exist any more, so fossils can show what life was like on Earth before humans existed.

How are fossils formed?

A creature dies

Fossils are most likely to form under water. First, an animal dies and sinks to the sea bed. Then it usually rots away, but sometimes the sea washes a layer of sediment (e.g. sand or mud) over it before it completely decays. The soft parts of the animal break down first, so often only its hard parts, like its skeleton or shell, are left.

The skeleton is covered in sediment

Next, the creature's bones slowly dissolve, and are replaced by minerals. Eventually, over a long period of time, these minerals harden into rock. This rock is called a fossil. It takes the same shape as the original bones, so the fossil looks the same as the skeleton of the animal.

The skeleton turns to rock

Since the soft parts of creatures break down first, most fossils only take the shape of the hard parts of creatures, such as bones, teeth and shells. However, on very rare occasions, an animal's remains are covered in sediment before the soft parts break down. This allows the soft parts to fossilise as well as the bones.

Mary looked up from the page, her mind racing. Could it be true? Were the curiosities she had been hunting since she was a little girl the remains of creatures from a different age?

The Student Becomes the Teacher

SEPTEMBER 1816 Mary put down the science article she was reading and rubbed her exhausted eyes. She was learning about different rocks and where they were found, but it was late, and the text was hard to understand. She got out her quill and some paper, and began to slowly copy out the article. The friend who had lent it to her would want it back soon, but if she had a copy, she could read it again and again.

Mary had a basic education from the local church Sunday school, but she had to teach herself all about geology and fossils.

Despite the care she had taken, Mary's small collection of geology books were now scruffy, worn and falling apart. They were also out of date. People were discovering new fossils all the time, and discussing them in meetings in London. Mary could only imagine what these gatherings were like — the rows of smartly dressed gentlemen, the buzz of geological chatter, the musty smell of the books and, above all, the wonderful fossils on display.

DECEMBER 1816 Mary bent lower over the kitchen table as she sliced into the cold flesh of the squid. A sharp stench filled the air and she wrinkled her nose. **Dissection** was a smelly hobby, but learning about modern creatures such as squid helped her understand the fossilised creatures, such as **belemnites** (bell-em-nights), that she found in the cliffs.

"Mary! I've told you a million times — no cuttin' things up in my kitchen!" her mother scolded.

"Sorry, Ma," Mary replied sheepishly. "It's so dark down in the workshop, I can't see what I'm doin'. And it's freezin'."

The tide would be out soon, so Mary tidied up and, glancing longingly at the blazing fire, dressed for the freezing conditions outside. They were short of money, so she needed to find some fossils to sell, and soon.

An artist's impression of an extinct belemnite.

18

SUMMER 1818 Together, the two fossil hunters paced along the beach, scanning the ground intently. Since she and Joseph had unearthed the mysterious creature, Mary had found several more in the cliffs. As her fame spread, a number of well-known scientists had come to visit her in Lyme, as well as enthusiastic collectors like Colonel Birch — her current companion.

She stooped to pick up a tiny ammonite fossil, and the Colonel raised his eyebrows.

"I don't know how you spot such small fossils, Mary. It really is exceptional."

"My pa taught me everythin' I know," Mary replied wistfully. "He were a much better fossil hunter than me. Here you are, sir — I've copied out the instructions he gave me."

She handed the Colonel a crumpled piece of paper.

How to Hunt for Fossils

To take full advantage of an outing, you will need to wear sturdy shoes. Bring a hammer with which to chip away rock; a basket or bag to carry your specimens; and a notebook and pencil to record where your fossils were found.

1. *Ensure that you have permission to remove fossils from the area you are hunting in. Ask permission of the landowner before you begin.*

2. *Check the time of the high tide. Leave the beach in good time to avoid being trapped by the rising water.*

3. *Search for fossils immediately after a large landslide. Search close to the bottom of the cliffs, amongst the debris. This is dangerous — avoid overhanging rock and places where the cliff is cracked; in these areas the cliff may be unstable.*

4. *Keep your eyes on the ground as you walk. Look for anything unusual, such as stones with odd shapes or colours.*

5. *With your hammer, gently tap rocks and try to break them open.*

6. *If you find a fossil, write down where you found it. Draw a sketch of its original location.*

7. *Identify your finds by comparing them to sketches of other fossils.*

An Invisible Woman

MAY 1819 Mary flicked through her notebook, scanning through some of the articles she had copied. They were all about the fossils she'd found — detailed descriptions of them, comparisons with other fossils that had been found and theories about how the creatures had lived. Her name wasn't mentioned in any of them.

At this time, women couldn't be scientists. They weren't allowed to go to university, and they were banned from institutions like the **Geological Society**.

As news of her fossil discoveries spread, more and more scientists were coming to visit her. They wanted to go out fossil hunting with her, or to buy her curiosities. Sometimes they even asked her for advice about different fossils. In return, she could find out what was happening in the scientific institutions of far-away London. However, there were long gaps between these visits, and she often didn't hear the latest geology news until months after it had been announced. As a woman — and a working-class woman at that — she was excluded from the scientific world.

Mary wandered along the familiar streets of Lyme towards the beach. She knew every stone of every street, every window of every house. She had never left Lyme Regis. Closing her eyes, she pictured London — the bustling, crowded streets; the smoking chimneys; the constant din of market sellers and carriages. Above all, she imagined wandering down the long corridors and through the huge rooms of the British Museum, pausing to examine the cases laden with fossils of every description.

Mary opened her eyes. Dreams were all very well, but they wouldn't pay the rent or put food on the table. With money tighter than ever, Mary couldn't afford to dream.

Visitors at the British Museum.

A Ray of Hope

JUNE 1819 A loud knock made Mary jump. Visitors were the very last thing she wanted. She opened the door to find her friend, Colonel Birch, on the doorstep.

"Things are a bit busy just now, sir," Mary stuttered, with as much dignity as she could muster. She tried to close the door on the chaos inside the house, but it was too late. Colonel Birch had seen the price labels she had attached to their old, battered furniture.

"Mary, whatever are you doing? Surely you're not selling your furniture?" he asked.

Slowly, reluctantly, she revealed her family's money troubles — how they hadn't found any valuable fossils for a year, and their rent was due.

"My dear Mary, this is terrible. I shall do what I can to help you," the Colonel promised.

July 1819

My dear James,

I am writing to urge you to join me in helping the distinguished fossil hunter, Mary Anning.

I have recently discovered that she desperately needs our help. Her family cannot pay the rent. They cannot afford food for their table, logs for their fire, or clothes for their backs. Would you let them starve? Would you allow them to end up on the street?

Without Mary Anning, a great many of our country's finest fossils would never have been found. We owe so much to the skill and effort of Miss Anning. How can we abandon her in her time of need?

Miss Anning deserves our help. She risks injury on a daily basis in order to snatch precious fossils from the greedy waves. She risks death in order to supply us with the fossils we want. She risks everything so that we don't have to.

I am determined to help Miss Anning, so I have decided to sell my fossil collection. All of the money raised will go to Mary Anning and her family. I implore you to come to the sale, and support this deserving geologist.

Yours affectionately,

Colonel T. Birch

False Accusations

DECEMBER 1823 Mary stormed into the kitchen and slammed a letter onto the table.

"They think my new fossil's fake!" she exclaimed.

Joseph looked puzzled. "Why would they say that?"

"They sent drawings of it to Mr Cuvier (Coo-vee-ay) — that famous scientist in Paris. He thinks we've tried to fool everyone by stickin' together the bodies of an ichthyosaur and a sea snake."

"But they believed us when we found the other monsters, even though we were just kids," he replied.

"Yes," Mary explained, "but he says it's impossible for a creature to have a neck this long — it's got a lot more **vertebrae** than anythin' that's been found before. But why would I make it up? I've got far too much to lose!"

It was so unfair. An accusation like this could ruin her reputation. If people stopped buying the large fossils she found, she'd be left combing the shores for small tourist trinkets. These barely made enough money to pay for food. The money Colonel Birch had raised from the fossil sale had long run out, and times were hard once more.

She vividly remembered finding the new fossil. At first she had thought that it was just another ichthyosaur. Then, as she chipped away at the stone surrounding it, she realised that its head was too small. Her heart had begun to race; this was something new. She had rushed back to town to get help to dig it out, leaving her dog, Tray, to guard her miraculous find.

Now, her joy had turned into despair. Instead of increasing her reputation, her discovery might actually destroy it.

The drawing on the right shows the fossil Mary was accused of forging — a plesiosaur (plee-zi-o-sore). The smaller picture shows what it might have looked like.

A Vital Clue

MARCH 1826 Walking down the steps to her workshop, Mary thought back to Mr Cuvier's accusation of forgery and smiled. As distressing as it had been two years ago, it had actually been good for business. Her scientist friends had defended her, and Mr Cuvier had finally admitted that he was wrong. As a result, Mary was considered an expert not only in finding fossils, but also in identifying them and setting them in plaster so they could be studied. Now, she was busier than ever. She had even been able to buy her own house in Lyme Regis, and convert the ground floor into a fossil shop.

Sitting down at her messy table, she got to work cleaning a beautiful ichthyosaur fossil, just two feet long. Suddenly, in the flickering shadows cast by her oil lamp, she noticed a small, dark object inside the animal's gut. She had suspected for a long time that the small stones often found next to animal fossils were actually their fossilised droppings, but she hadn't been able to prove it. Now, she had found the perfect piece of evidence. Grabbing a quill and paper, she began a letter to her friend, the famous geologist William Buckland.

DECEMBER 1826 Mary held her breath as William Buckland studied the fossil in silence. He hadn't believed her theory about these stones when she had written to him, but now he had seen this fossil, would he be convinced? After what seemed like hours, he began to speak:

"Mary, I think you may be right! These plain, dark stones could indeed be ancient droppings. I will have to look at this more closely. If you are right, this will be a remarkable discovery!"

"Let me show you the other examples I've found," she replied, her cheeks flushed with joy.

The two scientists spent hours examining the fossils together, and discussing Mary's theory. The sun was setting by the time Dr Buckland left. Mary smiled contentedly as she watched his carriage drive away.

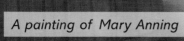

A painting of Mary Anning

Deadly Thunder

OCTOBER 1833 Mary walked purposefully along the beach, swinging her basket and hammer. She could feel the sun warming her back and taste the salty spray on her lips. Clouds wafted across the sapphire sky and squawking seagulls soared overhead.

Mary felt optimistic as she breathed in the scent of the damp clay. The recent heavy rain meant that there must have been some landslides, and landslides meant new fossils.

Scanning the cliff face, Mary searched for a good place to start. She spotted a pile of rocks which must have fallen from the cliff overnight. As she approached it, she wondered what she might find — a pretty ammonite, an ichthyosaur, maybe even another plesiosaur... She felt as if anything was possible.

The waves boomed against the shore, their white crests glittering in the sunlight. Over their din, Mary's well-trained ears caught a noise high up on the cliff. Her head whipped round to see a tiny line of pebbles tumbling from the cliff face only a few metres away. There was a loud crack. Time stood still. One word filled Mary's mind: *landslide*.

With a sickening groan, the whole surface of the cliff began to move. A tidal wave of rock and mud crashed to the beach below. Mary stumbled backwards, choking on the dust-filled air. She tripped and fell heavily, a sharp pain stabbing through her wrist. The world finally fell silent.

For a moment Mary lay still, her ears ringing. Slowly, painfully, she lifted her head and looked at the mounds of rubble and loose earth that surrounded her. With a sob, she hauled her legs free of their muddy tomb and staggered to her feet. She turned her back on the devastation and limped towards home, not caring what treasures had fallen from the treacherous cliff.

The cliffs at Lyme Regis, close to where the landslide happened.

Success At Last

JUNE 1839 Mary looked around her, taking in the familiar fossils displayed for sale on long wooden tables, the large window looking out onto the bustling street, and her work table in the corner, covered in new fossils waiting to be cleaned. Her shop was a success. She could live in comfort, and support her family as well. Her father would have been proud.

Her thoughts were interrupted by the tinkle of a bell — a customer!

Mary Anning (1799-1847)

Mary Anning was celebrated in the geological community during her lifetime, both for her ability to find fossils, and for her skill in preparing these fossils so other scientists could study them. Her work helped to shine a light on the **prehistoric** world, and she is now recognised as one of the most important women in the history of geology.

Why Were Her Discoveries Important?

Mary Anning found the first complete fossils of two types of **marine** reptiles: ichthyosaurs (with her brother) and plesiosaurs. She also unearthed a pterosaur (terro-sore) — a flying reptile — and several types of fossil fish. All of these creatures lived over 65 million years ago, during the time of the dinosaurs (although they weren't actually dinosaurs).

At the time, people knew almost nothing about ancient reptiles; only fragments had been found before. Mary's complete fossils allowed scientists to study these creatures in much greater detail.

A dinosaur fossil.

© iStockphoto.com/Andrew_Howe

During the early 1800s, Mary Anning's discoveries, as well as discoveries of dinosaur fossils, helped scientists understand that the Earth was much older than people thought. The Bible taught that it was only a few thousand years old, but scientists now knew that it must be much older.

What Other Contributions Did She Make?

Mary Anning's discovery of the fossilised droppings of ancient marine reptiles hugely increased scientists' understanding of prehistoric creatures, particularly their diets.

She also identified ink sacs inside belemnite fossils. She encouraged people in Lyme Regis to grind up the fossilised ink, mix it with water and use it to draw pictures to sell to tourists.

A painting from 1830 showing many of Mary's discoveries.

© Pictorial Press Ltd / Alamy

How Was She Honoured After Her Death?

- In 1848, her friend Henry de la Beche, then President of the Geological Society, published a speech about her life in the Society's journal.
- In the church in Lyme Regis, there is a stained glass window dedicated to Mary Anning's memory, which was paid for by the Geological Society.
- There are two species of fossil fish and a type of reptile named after her.

Glossary

belemnites — Squid-like creatures that are now extinct

dissection — Cutting up dead animals or plants to learn about their structure

fossils — The remains of animals or plants preserved in rock

Geological Society — A group of men who met to discuss geology

geology — The scientific study of rocks

marine — To do with the sea

prehistoric — Something that existed before humans started to write down history

vertebrae — Bones which make up the spine

Charles Darwin

"The father of evolution"

written by Anthony Muller

SEPTEMBER 1817 Charley sneaked a look at the iced cakes that lay in the shop window. Their white peaks glistened with sugary goodness, and he licked his lips. He took a deep breath and glanced at Mr Rothschild, the shopkeeper. It was now or never.

Charley carefully picked up two cakes. Mr Rothschild eyed him with the special sort of suspicion that shopkeepers reserve exclusively for young troublemakers. Charley reached up to his hat, and remembered what his friend, Garnett, had said.

"You jus' got to tip the hat a bit, then pull it down sorta over your right eye. All the shops know it means you knew my grandpa, and they'll let you have stuff for nothing."

Looking directly at Mr Rothschild, Charley followed Garnett's instructions, and then headed towards the shop's exit.

"Oi!" Mr Rothschild shouted, as he came after Charley with loud, clumping footsteps and a thick, outstretched arm. He was on Charley in seconds.

Terrified, Charley dropped the cakes and ran out of the shop, speeding past Garnett, who was in fits of laughter.

© SCIENCE PHOTO LIBRARY

Charles's father, Robert Darwin, was a respected doctor. He was very strict, but Charles said he was the kindest man he had ever known.

It had been a difficult few months for Charley. First, his father had forced him to start school, which he hated — it was no fun at all. Then, just as he'd got over this traumatic experience, his mother had suddenly died.

It was two months since she had passed away, and thinking of her still brought a tear to his eye. She had been an important part of his upbringing — dragging him and his siblings to church every week, rain or shine. Now, with his father busy with work, his bossy older sisters were in charge of making sure Charles behaved himself. He wasn't going to make it easy for them.

Charles was only 8 when his mother died.

A Disgrace to the Family

JUNE 1830 Tearing a strip of bark from the tree, Charles couldn't believe his luck. Three rare beetles lurked underneath. Charles quickly grabbed the first two, but he didn't have enough hands for the third. Without thinking, he put one of the beetles in his mouth and went after the remaining beetle.

Suddenly, his tongue began to burn, and a horrible stench filled his nostrils. Charles spat out the beetle, and fell to the forest floor, retching. The beetles made their escape.

Beetle collecting was a huge craze during the early 1800s. Collectors competed to get the biggest and best beetle collections.

Lying on the ground, staring up at the light that filtered through the leafy canopy, Charles couldn't help but feel guilty about having skipped his university work to go beetle collecting — again. He thought of how furious his father would be if he'd known, and recalled something that he'd once told him as a boy:

> ***"You care for nothing but shooting, dogs, and rat-catching, and you will be a disgrace to yourself and all your family."***

On reflection, not much had changed.

AUGUST 1831 Back at home in Shrewsbury, Charles held a mysterious letter in his hands, his face a picture of pure puzzlement. He carefully opened the letter and saw it was from one of his professors. Charles read the letter hungrily, and curiosity quickly turned to excitement.

His fingers shook as he reread the last paragraph again and again. 'So, when asked to recommend someone to be the HMS Beagle's **naturalist** on its round-the-world voyage, you immediately sprang to mind. I recall how much time at Cambridge you spent outside studying nature, when you were meant to be inside, studying **theology**. If you're interested, the job's yours.' How could Charles refuse? It was the opportunity of a lifetime...

A young Charles Darwin.

A Voyage into the Unknown

27ᵀᴴ DECEMBER 1831 Standing on the deck of the Beagle, Charles gazed out across the grey waters of Plymouth Harbour and told his already queasy stomach to behave itself. Their departure had been delayed twice by storms, but they were finally ready to set off.

31st December 1831 — We have only been at sea for four days, yet I am already regretting this venture — I find myself almost constantly sick. Captain FitzRoy and I are getting along well. He is an intelligent, handsome gentleman, who often speaks his thoughts — just today he told me he does not like the shape of my nose!

15th January 1832 — I have decided to carry on the journey, despite my continuing illness. I am determined not to squander this opportunity. Father would be most displeased if I neglected my duties again, particularly as he has paid for my passage.

*28th February — My blood boils violently as I write this. Captain FitzRoy and I had a furious row today about slavery in Salvador. I said it was an **abomination**, but he stubbornly claimed that the slaves were happy! A great many words were said in anger, and FitzRoy has since banned me from his dinner table.*

25th October — I have had word that the fossils I sent home in August were previously unknown — remarkable! I feel as if I am really doing something worthwhile.

4th March 1833 — Today I visited the Falkland Islands and brought back some fossils. Amazingly, they were very different from those I uncovered in Argentina. There may be value in comparing the various fossils and wildlife of each region we visit.

10th September — I keep wondering at the sheer size of the fossils I have collected. One does not see giant creatures like these any more. Why did these animals become extinct? Was it a change in their environment? I do not know...

13th October 1834 — I have been bedridden for the last two weeks with a fever so awful I thought I was sure to die. I am told the cause was likely an insect bite, yet it is hard to believe an insect could inflict such misery. I am only now strong enough to take hold of a pen. A good deal of rest seems to have seen me through the worst of it.

19th September 1835 — We have been in the Galapagos Islands for three days, and I have noticed something strange. Many of the birds look almost identical (and one might think that they are all the same species) except that some have thin beaks, others have large beaks. It is most perplexing. I should like to study this in more detail.

On the Home Stretch

NOVEMBER 25ᵀᴴ 1835 As the sailors helped the large, awkward frame of Queen Pomare clamber aboard the Beagle, Charles had no idea what to expect. All of his **preconceptions** about the Tahitians had already proved false in the last few days.

He had been told the Beagle would receive a rough and uncivilised welcome, yet nothing could have been further from the truth. They had been greeted with cheers and smiling faces, and Charles had found the Tahitians to be friendly, sensible and well-mannered.

Queen Pomare IV

© age fotostock Spain, S.L. / Alamy

Over dinner, Charles couldn't help but compare Queen Pomare to the English royals. Next to them, she had virtually no grace or dignity, but Charles did notice one thing that showed she was of royal blood: her face remained unmoved by the evening's entertainment. Neither the dinner they provided, nor the gifts, nor the firework display raised a smile. Yet, she was not ungrateful — she was simply maintaining royal appearances. Thinking of the English royals was enough to make Charles homesick, and with at least another few months at sea, he tried to push thoughts of England out of his mind.

© iStockphoto.com/rusm

On the Beagle's voyage, Charles not only studied, but also ate many of the strange creatures that he saw. This included armadillos, iguanas, giant tortoises and a puma.

5ᵀᴴ OCTOBER 1836 The Darwin family sat down to breakfast, and watched hungrily as their servants brought in steaming pots of tea, large bowls of fruit and huge plates laden with eggs, bacon and haddock.

Robert Darwin was about to tuck into the plate of food sat before him when the dining room doors abruptly swung open. As the new arrival strolled into the room, Robert squinted at the man. His smiling face seemed oddly familiar. It couldn't be, could it? Scarcely believing his eyes, he laughed loudly, stood up and embraced his son.

"My Charley, home at last! I must say that I am most proud of you. Many great men have written to tell me you are very clever. Come now, after five years away, you must be starving."

A Matter of the Heart

SEPTEMBER 1837 Charles stumbled slightly. He grabbed hold of his desk to steady himself. Pages from his new book tumbled to the floor as he clutched at his chest. He was struggling to breathe. Between gasps for air, Charles begged his maid to call for a doctor.

Charles was plagued by a mysterious illness almost all of his adult life. Nowadays, many doctors believe it was probably caused by an insect bite that occurred on his round-the-world trip.

After Charles had returned from his trip, he had been paid a large sum of money to publish a series of books based on the journals and notes he had written on board the Beagle. For almost a year, he had done nothing but work on these books, making them suitable for publication. It had clearly taken its toll.

As his vision started to go, Charles tried to focus on the pages that now lay scattered on the floor. Suddenly they seemed to be getting closer...

He lost consciousness.

ONE MONTH LATER, and Charles was sick of Staffordshire, and everything it had to offer. It was all very well for doctors to recommend a holiday in the countryside, but didn't they realise how boring it was? He couldn't wait to get back to work.

The only consolation was the presence of his cousin, Emma. She was a kind, charming and attractive woman, and Charles had grown very fond of her.

Emma was a very caring woman who spent most of her days looking after her ill mother, but she never once complained. Unlike the rest of his relatives, who constantly badgered Charles about his experiences at sea, Emma was thoughtful enough to leave him in peace. Yet whenever Charles spoke about his theories, she always listened attentively, and asked searching questions about things that Charles had not even considered.

Over the last few weeks they had shared a great many smiles over the breakfast table, and Charles wondered whether there could be something more between them than just friendship.

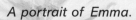
A portrait of Emma.

A Difference of Opinion

MARCH 1838 The more Charles thought about the marvels of his Beagle trip, the more curious he became about how different species had developed. He began to research the opinions of others to see if he could find an answer.

Before Darwin, how did people think species developed?

Whilst Darwin was developing his own theory, he read a lot of other people's ideas (both religious and scientific) to see whether he thought they had any merit.

In the 19th century, the Christian Church taught that God created every species to be perfectly adapted to their environment. This meant that they never needed to change — every species that existed had always stayed the same.

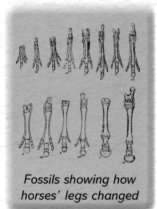

Fossils showing how horses' legs changed

However, some scientists argued that there seemed to be evidence that species hadn't stayed the same. In the 19th century, lots of new fossils were discovered, which scientists believed showed some species at different stages of development. This suggested that species *were* changing.

Many religious people argued that all the different species must have been created by God because the natural world was so complicated. Things like eyes seemed too complex to have developed randomly.

On the other hand, scientists came up with different explanations for how things like eyes had developed. One of these theories was called transmutation. Scientists such as Jean-Baptiste Lamarck argued that species naturally changed because of their environment. For example, giraffes were constantly stretching their neck muscles to reach higher leaves. This made their necks grow slightly longer, and when the giraffes had offspring the young giraffes inherited their parents' slightly longer necks.

Jean-Baptiste Lamarck

Neither the religious or scientific theories were able to convince everybody that they were correct. People still disagreed about how different species developed.

A Practical Marriage

25ᵀᴴ NOVEMBER 1838 Charles groaned in agony as the stabbing pain returned to his stomach once more. The doctor peered down at him thoughtfully, and Charles felt the cold touch of the stethoscope on his chest again.

He stared up at the miserable ceiling. It had become far too familiar this past year. Charles was frustrated — not a single doctor could give him a diagnosis, and all they prescribed was rest. How could he rest when he had such important things to do?

After the doctor left, Charles forced himself out of bed. He was meant to be house-hunting for himself and Emma, but in the two weeks since their engagement he had been almost constantly ill. He hoped it wasn't a bad omen for their marriage.

No — Charles stopped this train of thought dead in its tracks. Bad omen or not, illness and work had delayed their marriage long enough, and he wasn't going to put up with it any more.

When deciding whether to wed Emma, Charles made lists for and against marrying. One of the things he wrote in favour of marriage was 'constant companion... better than a dog anyhow'.

JANUARY 1839 Sharing a kiss with Emma for the first time as husband and wife, all of Charles's pre-wedding nerves vanished — he knew he'd made the right choice.

There was no time for a honeymoon. A train was to whisk the newly-weds straight to London, where Charles planned to spend the next few weeks finishing off his Beagle journals for publication.

AUGUST 1839 Had all the months of work been worth it? Charles thought so. Only a few months after his *Journal and Remarks* had gone on sale, all of the copies had sold out — it was already being reprinted. His publisher told him that he was now famous, whatever that meant! Fame, although it had its benefits, didn't really matter to Charles. What mattered was that the book's sales gave him a steady income to finance his studies, and support his wife.

Evolution of an Idea

AUGUST 1847 As Charles explained his unfinished theory to Emma, he worried about how she'd react. Emma was very religious, and Charles knew that his theory could be seen as **heresy** — the Church taught that God created all animals perfectly, so they didn't need to change. Charles was arguing that creatures changed to survive.

After Charles had finished, Emma told him she would always support him. However, he could tell she was concerned. If his theory was heresy, they would be separated in the afterlife — Charles would go to hell, whilst Emma went to heaven.

Charles Darwin's Theory of Evolution

Darwin came up with a new explanation for how different species had developed. He thought that in nature every animal was competing for limited resources; for example, giraffes compete for leaves. He also thought that each animal population had natural variations (or differences); for example, giraffes have different lengths of neck. This idea was different from transmutation because transmutation suggested that animals (like the giraffes) caused these variations themselves by their behaviour.

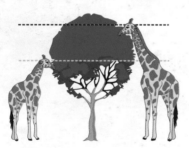

The tall giraffe can reach all the leaves below the red line.

The short giraffe can only reach leaves below the blue line.

Some natural variations are more useful than others. For example, a longer neck is more useful to a giraffe than a shorter neck because a longer neck means they can reach higher leaves. The more leaves a giraffe can reach, the more likely it is that it will survive.

Animals that are better adapted to their surroundings will probably survive longer than those which aren't as well adapted. This means they will probably have more offspring in their lifespan. These offspring inherit the useful variation, and because they would probably also live longer, they too are likely to have more offspring. Therefore the useful variation gradually spreads. Eventually this could cause a whole new species to develop.

Lifespan of 15 years — fewer offspring.

Lifespan of 25 years — more offspring.

A Death in the Family

NOVEMBER 1849 Annie finished playing with Charles's hair and declared it beautiful. She straightened his collar and then jumped off his lap, skipping across the drawing room to join the rest of her brothers and sisters.

Like most of the people they knew, Charles and Emma had a large family. They had six children, three boys and three girls, and a seventh on the way. Charles didn't play favourites, but Annie was perhaps the loveliest of all his children. He could not help grinning whenever he saw her, whether she was drawing, playing the piano or just reading quietly.

*Charles was an unusually attentive father for a Victorian gentleman. Many men left the upbringing of their children to their wife or a **governess**.*

Charles looked around at his family, and was filled with joy. Annie met his gaze, and her eyes twinkled as she smiled back at him. He felt like the luckiest man alive. As Charles wondered at the happy life they had built for themselves, only the sound of Annie coughing interrupted the sound of the children playing.

© English Heritage

The Darwins lost three children at a young age, but Annie's death hit the family hardest of all. The sense of loss was so great that none of them could bear to attend her funeral. Charles was never able to face visiting her grave.

APRIL 1851 Charles wept as he embraced Annie's frail body. She'd only just turned ten — she'd barely lived! How could God take her away? It was too much for him to take, and he cried uncontrollably into the bedsheets.

Long after the candles had burnt out, Charles sat in the dark of his daughter's room. He had not been to church for almost two years, but he had continued to believe in God. However, Annie's death was causing him to seriously question his faith. As he clutched her cold, still hand, he wondered if he wanted to believe in a God who would take away the life of such a kind and innocent girl.

He knew that if he told his family about his religious doubts, he would only upset them. So, in the blackness of the night, Charles decided to keep his concerns to himself for now.

A New Chapter

JUNE 1858 Charles paused, took a deep breath, and reread the theory of evolution that lay before him. Butterflies performed somersaults in his stomach. It was well-written, logical and ready to be published. There was only one problem — it wasn't his.

This was the work of a scientist named Alfred Russel Wallace. Charles had spent so long trying to perfect his own theory that someone else had beaten him to the punch. Luckily, Wallace had not yet shared his work with the world — he had sent his ideas to Charles to ask him if he thought they had any value.

*Charles spent years gathering careful evidence of evolution, including eight years (between 1846 and 1854) just studying **barnacles**.*

Charles felt sick. Why hadn't he published his theory earlier? His friends had warned him that the more he delayed, the more risk there was of someone else coming to the same conclusions, but Charles hadn't listened. How he wished he had listened now.

23ᴿᴰ NOVEMBER 1859 The more he thought about it, the more Charles thought Wallace's letter had been a blessing in disguise. Who knows how long he might have spent gathering evidence had it not been for Wallace? Despite his initial distress, Charles had never considered ignoring Wallace's work, and they had eventually published a short article together.

Wallace's letter had finally forced him to finish his book, *On the Origin of Species*, which contained Charles's theory of evolution. The book was to go on sale tomorrow, and Charles was unable to sleep. Charles hoped it would totally dwarf his and Wallace's article. Whilst their joint article had been fairly rushed, this book was the result of over twenty years' work. As the sun slowly peeked his head over the horizon, Charles knew that only time would tell.

Fame, Fortune and Controversy

24ᵀᴴ NOVEMBER 1859 Francis, one of Charles's sons, stood at the door of the study, out of breath and unable to speak. After an age, he finally found his voice.

"Father," he began, his voice breaking as he spoke, "I went to the shop to get another copy of your book, just as you asked. And... and—"

"What is it boy? Speak up!" Charles told him. Terrifying visions flashed before his eyes: rioting, angry mobs, piles of his books on fire.

"There was a problem. I couldn't get a copy. The book... It's—"

"A problem? What's happened?" The lump in Charles's throat got bigger.

"The book... It's sold out! I'm sorry, father."

Laughing, Charles picked up his son and swung him around, his eyes filling with tears of joy.

DECEMBER 1859 A month later, and Charles was surprised that the book hadn't actually caused much outrage at all. Of course, there were those who were appalled by his ideas — who thought that he was challenging religion — but many people seemed to accept his theory. Charles was incredibly relieved, especially as he had never set out to attack religion; he had simply set out to uncover the truth of how different species came to be.

Charles's success made him dare to go further. He had a theory that humans had evolved from apes, but he had not mentioned it in *On the Origin of Species* in case it was too controversial. The Bible said that God had created humans "in his own image", but if humans were originally apes, it raised questions about whether humans really were special — it meant they were basically just animals.

Now, he wondered if the world might be ready after all.

Making History

FEBRUARY 1871 Charles held one of the first copies of *The Descent of Man* and absent-mindedly leafed through the pages of his new book. He felt like his whole life had been building up to this moment — this was it; this was his life's work.

The Cambridge Star

9ᵗʰ March 1871
Price 1d

LETTERS TO THE EDITOR

Dear Sir — I was shocked to hear of the publication of Mr Darwin's disgusting book *The Descent of Man*. His arguments are clearly designed to undermine the church's teachings. It is nothing but stuff and nonsense, and as a Christian, I was appalled by the publisher's decision to print the book. Publishers have a responsibility to protect society from harmful and immoral ravings such as this. How can anyone even consider the idea that humans are related to apes? If people have any sense at all, they should avoid going anywhere near this despicable work. With any luck, both Mr Darwin and his publisher will be left out of pocket. *Yours faithfully, Alex Winterburn.*

Mr Darwin — the talk of the town.

Dear Sir — I was fortunate to pick up one of the first copies of Mr Darwin's *The Descent of Man*, and I find it revolutionary, remarkable and above all reasonable. Who could argue with the logic of Darwin's theory? I would recommend that anyone and everyone read this fascinating work. Get your hands on a copy however you can — buy it, borrow it or steal it, but for goodness' sake, read it as soon as possible. You mustn't miss out on such an important work! *Yours truly, George Dixon.*

Dear Sir — I am a Christian, and I bought a copy of *The Descent of Man* fearing the worst. I expected to see an attack on Christian beliefs, but having read this work I am more intrigued than outraged. I cannot see any good reason why my religious beliefs should not sit alongside the scientific theory laid out in the book. Who is to say that natural selection isn't part of God's plan?

My experience leads me to give your readers the following advice: shrug off your preconceptions, buy the book, and make up your own mind. The idea that humans came from apes may sound crazy, and you might disagree, but you should at least read the evidence before you dismiss it. You may be surprised... *Yours faithfully, Jon Adams.*

Standing the Test of Time

19ᵀᴴ APRIL 1882 Charles lay limp and lifeless on the bed, and knew the end was coming. Throughout his life, he had suffered constant aches and pains, but this was different. He lifted his heavy eyelids, and saw Emma beside him. She forced a smile when she realised he was awake.

In his life, Charles had achieved many great things. He may have even changed the face of human history forever — but now, as he lay on his death bed, he wasn't thinking about his achievements, his awards or his work. He thought only of his wife and his family.

He summoned the last of his energy, looked Emma in the eye and managed to croak out a few words.

Charles's theory of evolution wasn't the first to deal with how different species came to be, but it was the first one to be widely accepted by the scientific community. 150 years on, it is still the leading theory about how life on Earth developed.

> ## "Remember what a good wife you have been to me — tell all my children to remember how good they have been to me."

As Emma strained to hear him, Charles breathed his last breath.

Glossary

abomination — A terrible outrage

barnacles — A type of small shellfish that attaches itself to rocks

governess — A woman who teaches children in a wealthy household

heresy — An idea that goes against what the church teaches

naturalist — Someone who studies nature

preconceptions — Beliefs held without actual knowledge or experience of something

theology — The study of God and religion

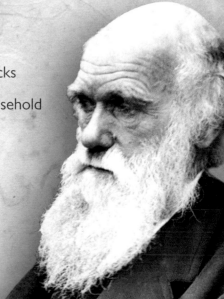

Marie Curie

"The radioactive woman"

written by Claire Boulter

MAY 1872 Glancing quickly around to see that nobody was watching, four-year-old Marie Sklodovska (Skwad-off-ska) crept through the door and closed it softly behind her. Her heart hammering with excitement, she tiptoed across the worn rug to the far corner of the room. There, like a cave crammed with treasure, stood the locked case containing her father's science equipment. Wide-eyed, Marie leaned closer, her breath misting the polished glass. She had no idea what the glass jars and shining metal instruments were for, but they fascinated her.

"Manya!" Marie jumped as her father's gently chiding voice interrupted her daydream. "Whatever are you doing in here? Come on, little one, it's bedtime for you."

*Marie's family lived in Warsaw, Poland. At the time it was part of the **Russian Empire**. Children weren't allowed to learn Polish history, language or practical science. Marie's father, a science teacher, brought his equipment home to keep it safe.*

SIX YEARS LATER Despite the warmth of the day, Marie huddled between her father and brother as they stood beside the freshly dug grave. For as long as Marie could remember, her mother had been pale, thin and racked by fits of painful coughing as **tuberculosis** (tube-erk-yule-o-sis) ravaged her lungs. Yet Marie had never imagined that she would be taken from them so soon. As the priest began his mournful sermon, Marie clutched at her father's hand and retreated into her private world. She imagined she was a doctor — a genius — who had invented a miracle cure for illness. There would be no more suffering, no more death...

Marie with her brother and two of her sisters. Left to right: Bronya, Joseph, Marie, Helen. Her oldest sister, Sophie, died when Marie was eight.

40

The Perilous Path to Knowledge

FEBRUARY 1890 Marie collapsed onto her bed, her body shaking. Now that she was able to relax the sobs began, and for several minutes she abandoned herself to them. It was so unfair! Why should she have to risk imprisonment to get an education?

If only she could talk to Bronya — her sister could always cheer her up. She wiped her eyes; she would write instead.

It was illegal for women to go to university in Poland. Marie attended the 'Floating University' — a group who met to learn in secret.

Novolipki Street, Warsaw
8th February 1890

My dearest Bronya,

How are you? Tell me all the news from Paris. You have no idea how I envy you, studying at the university there! I long to learn without having to hide, without living in constant fear of arrest.

We had a near miss tonight, and I was badly shaken by it. I attended a lecture — this evening it was Mademoiselle Antek's turn to host it. I always thought we'd be safe from the Russian police at her house.

The lecture itself was fascinating; we debated mathematics late into the evening — heaven! However, as we were about to leave there came a loud banging at the door. I heard someone shout and there was sudden chaos as we all scrambled to get out. The hallway was dark, and I stumbled and twisted my ankle. I thought I'd never reach the back door, but suddenly I was outside! I ran all the way home, my sore ankle threatening to give way with every step. I swear I didn't breathe until I had closed the front door behind me!

I know I'm fortunate to be able to attend these lectures, but I can't help resenting how hard it is to gain an education. I feel that I could do some good in the world, if only I could study medicine or the sciences properly. I'm just glad that, by working and saving, I'm able to help you through university. I cling to the thought that, once you are qualified as a doctor and are earning enough to help me, I'll be able to join you in Paris — what bliss that will be!

With great affection, Manya

A Taste of Freedom

OCTOBER 1891 Squashed between a toothless old woman who mumbled continuously and a fat man who smelt of goats, Marie craned her neck to peer out of the foggy train window at the landscape trundling by. The fourth-class carriage from Warsaw to Paris was hardly luxurious, with its hard wooden benches and overpowering odour of dirt and people, but to Marie it seemed like paradise.

*For six years before she left for Paris, Marie worked as a **governess** and a tutor. She used her wages to help Bronya go to university.*

At last, Bronya was settled and had a steady income, so she had invited Marie to live with her in Paris. Marie would finally know what it meant to live in a free country; she would be free to speak as she wished and believe whatever she chose. Best of all, she would be free to study science!

JULY 1892 Standing up from her desk, Marie swayed and clutched the back of her chair. When had she last eaten? She remembered having a slice of bread and butter yesterday, but since then she had been too busy working to think about food. She made her way shakily to the food cupboard. Inside were two shrivelled radishes. With a sigh she put them on her plate and sat down again at her desk; she would go shopping when she had more money and less to do. Who needed food when there was so much to learn?

A YEAR LATER Marie closed her eyes, ignoring the crush and babble of students around her. In a moment the results of their final exams would be read out in order, from best to worst. She had worked so hard for this, but had she done enough to pass her degree?

A breathless hush descended on the room as the examiner strode onto the stage. He cleared his throat and spoke.

"First in class, Marie Sklodovska."

Marie (left) found that Bronya's flat was too far from university, so she moved closer. Paying rent meant she had little money left.

A Mutual Magnetism

JANUARY 1894 Marie paused outside the parlour door, tucked a stray strand of hair behind her ear and took a deep breath. She had recently started some research on the magnetic properties of steel, but she had run out of space to work. Her friend, Professor Kovalski (Kov-al-ski), had offered to introduce her to a physicist who might be able to help.

Entering the room timidly, she was greeted by the warm smile of the professor.

"My dear Marie!" he said eagerly. "Let me introduce you to a friend of mine."

Marie felt her cheeks redden as the dark-haired man turned from the window to face her. How ridiculous! She had no interest in love; her work was all that mattered. Yet the way he took her hand, the way he held her gaze made her heart flutter like a trapped bird.

"This," said Professor Kovalski, "is Pierre Curie."

"...his smile, at once grave and young, inspired confidence."

26TH JULY 1895 Marie woke to a shaft of sunshine caressing her cheek. Drowsily, she began to contemplate the day's work; she would order some new steel samples and... wait! With a jolt, she remembered what day it was. There would be no work today, because in a few hours she and Pierre were getting married. By the end of the day she would no longer be Marie Sklodovska, she would be Marie Curie. How strange that sounded!

Marie leapt from her bed and flung open the window to breathe in the sweet morning air. For a year she had refused Pierre's proposal, hoping that she could move back to Poland one day. But gradually she had come to realise that she needed him. He would be more than a husband — their aims, their ideals and their passion for science were so closely matched. Together, they would achieve so much!

Marie and Pierre spent their honeymoon cycling in France.

An Element of Doubt

NOVEMBER 1897 Marie pushed aside the stack of paper and sighed. She had been reading solidly for weeks, trying to find a subject for her **thesis**, but nothing seemed quite right. Suddenly, her eye was caught by a paper published the previous year — a physicist called Becquerel (Beck-er-ell) had found that a **chemical element** called uranium (you-rain-ee-um) emitted strange rays of energy. Nobody knew what these rays were, or where they came from. Her mind started to spin with the possibilities — suppose she found something entirely new to science? Now that would be worthwhile!

FEBRUARY 1898 Oblivious to the cold and damp of the cramped room, Marie felt her hands begin to tremble. She had checked her results again and again. There could be no mistake: the mineral she was testing emitted much stronger rays than anything known to science. The hairs stood up on the back of her neck as she realised what this meant. She had found a new element.

The university wouldn't give Marie a proper laboratory, so she worked in a storeroom in the Physics building.

JULY 1900 Marie turned from the vat of boiling acid she had been stirring for the past four hours, and pressed her hands into the small of her back. She contemplated the mountain of rocky debris that she still had to process.

"My love," Pierre's voice murmured in her ear, "you look exhausted. Would it not be better to postpone this research until we have a better laboratory?"

Pierre was so intrigued by Marie's work that he gave up his own research to help her.

"No!" Marie said fiercely. "We have to extract more of our new element — until we do other scientists will never believe that it exists. We must go on."

The Curies processed about three tons of this rock (pitchblende) — grinding it, dissolving it in acid and drying it time after time — to obtain one-tenth of a gram of the new element (radium).

JANUARY 1902 Back at home after a long day at work, Marie couldn't sit still. She paced the floor, glancing every now and then at the clock. Earlier that day, they had finally done it — they had isolated enough radium to prove that it existed. Nobody could doubt it now!

"Pierre," she said suddenly, "let's go back to the lab, just for a little while."

The laboratory was dark as Marie slipped her key into the lock. Stepping through the doorway, she suddenly stopped.

"Look!" she breathed. All around them, from each tiny glass vial of radium, came a soft, blue glow. The room twinkled as though hundreds of fireflies had gathered there.

WHAT IS RADIOACTIVITY?

When Marie Curie first saw her glowing vials of radium, they were releasing a mysterious energy — nobody knew what it was or where it came from. So what was going on?

WHAT ARE ATOMS?

Atoms are minute pieces of matter. There are different types of atoms. These different types are called elements. Atoms are like tiny building blocks — everything in the universe is made up of atoms of different elements arranged in different combinations.

HOW DO ATOMS RELEASE ENERGY?

Many atoms are stable — they stay the same under almost all conditions. However, some atoms are unstable — in elements such as radium, the atom is too heavy to hold together, so it breaks apart. When it breaks apart it gives out energy. This energy is called radiation, and the process of releasing it is called radioactivity.

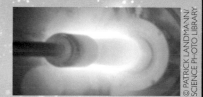

The energy given off by some unstable atoms makes them glow.

© PATRICK LANDMANN/ SCIENCE PHOTO LIBRARY

WHAT DID MARIE CURIE DO?

Marie wasn't the first scientist to observe radioactivity, but she was the first to realise that radiation came from atoms. She even came up with the name 'radioactivity', which comes from the Latin word 'radius', meaning 'ray'.

Marie Curie had discovered something new and exciting — that the atoms of some elements could release energy. We now know that her finding has lots of important uses.

© iStockphoto.com/clearviewstock

Delight and Disaster

JUNE 1903 Marie sat quietly in the front row of the lecture theatre, listening proudly as Pierre described their research to the enthralled crowd. As his session drew to a close, Pierre rolled up his shirt sleeve, revealing a livid burn mark.

"This burn," he said softly, "is the result of binding a small amount of radium to my arm for ten hours. The radium killed the skin, but our studies show that it kills diseased tissue faster than healthy tissue. Because of this, my wife and I believe that radium may provide a way of treating that terrible curse on our society: **cancer**."

*As a woman, Marie wasn't allowed to present her research herself. However, in 1903 she and Pierre were awarded a **Nobel Prize** — the first time that a woman had won one.*

As the audience applauded, Marie felt a warm wave of pleasure break over her. Who could have guessed that radium could do so much good?

"our discovery is a blessing for humanity... it permits the reduction of human suffering and treatment of a terrible disease."

19ᵀᴴ APRIL 1906 Arriving home, Marie listed to herself all the things she had to do that evening: bathe the girls, repair Pierre's trousers, start making a new dress for Eve... Her work as a wife and mother was never done. She closed the door behind her, and only then noticed Pierre's friend and colleague, Paul Appell, standing in the hallway, his face stricken. He began to speak. Marie, adrift on a dark sea of dread, heard only isolated snatches.

"Pierre... horse-drawn wagon... stepped out without looking... skull crushed... killed instantly."

Struggling to make sense of his words, Marie could only whisper, "Pierre is dead? Dead? Absolutely dead?"

Pierre's death left Marie to raise their two children, Eve (left) and Irene (right), on her own.

© Photos.com/Thinkstock

46

Life After Death

A MONTH LATER Marie sat blank-faced before a panel of professors from the University.

Peering kindly at the severe looking woman in front of him, the head of the science department reflected how thin and pale she looked. Still, she was made of stern stuff, and undoubtedly she would bounce back, given time. He cleared his throat.

"Madame," he began, "since the tragic loss of your husband, our department has suffered. There is nobody among our remaining professors who fully understands his research or can teach it to our students. I have sought the opinions of my colleagues, and we all agree that you are the only person fit to take over Pierre's job. Are you willing to become the first female professor at the University of Paris?"

Marie bowed her head. She used to dream of this moment; she had just never imagined it would happen like this. Could she do it? She could barely get through each day. And yet... wouldn't this be a fitting tribute to Pierre? Her eyes still downcast, she finally spoke.

"I will try."

NOVEMBER 1911 Standing on the Rue Pierre Curie, Marie gazed at the bare skeleton of the part-finished building opposite, swarming with workmen. When it was finished, this would be her research centre; great scientists would gather here to study radioactivity and its medical uses.

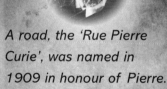

A road, the 'Rue Pierre Curie', was named in 1909 in honour of Pierre. In 1967 it was renamed 'Rue Pierre et Marie Curie'.

Marie still felt as though her heart had been buried with Pierre. But beneath her grief, she felt a faint glow of pride: finally the University was taking her research seriously. Finally, she would have a laboratory worthy of Pierre's memory.

The Radium Institute in Paris was completed in July 1914.

The Miracle Cure

July 1914 In the newly finished Radium Institute, a solitary figure drifted from room to room, pausing to inhale the smell of fresh paint and to gaze out through the huge windows. Since the discovery of radium, Marie's fame had grown until she sometimes felt she was drowning in a sea of invitations to give lectures and open public buildings. Opportunities to be alone were few, and she welcomed this one.

Soon, the rooms would be full of people and equipment, the hustle and bustle of scientists labouring to unlock the secrets of radium.

There were many claims about the healing powers of radium; people believed it could cure everything from toothache to tuberculosis.

We now know that, although radium can be used to treat cancer, it doesn't cure other illnesses, and can be very harmful.

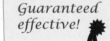

A Matter of Life and Death

3ʳᵈ AUGUST 1914 Marie paced feverishly from one side of the small room to the other. She had known this moment was coming, but it was still a shock. The Germans had declared war on France; unless they were defeated, the country that she had grown to love, to view as home, would be destroyed. She must do something to help, but what?

World War I lasted from 1914 to 1918. It was one of the biggest and deadliest conflicts in history, with more than 8.5 million soldiers killed.

Marie stopped mid-stride as inspiration struck. Of course! Around the same time as she had discovered radium, another scientist had discovered rays that could be used to take pictures inside the body. How valuable such science would be on the **front line**!

DECEMBER 1914 6 a.m., a few days after Christmas. The room is still and cold. Marie bursts in, laden with equipment. First: cover the windows, make the room light-proof. Next: set up the X-ray equipment. Then: connect the equipment to the van engine to power it. Shouts from outside. Barely time to connect the last wire before the casualty is carried in.

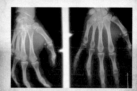

The equipment that Marie developed used X-rays. These pass through soft tissue (e.g. muscle), but not through hard material like bone or bullets. Pictures taken with X-rays show these hard bits.

He groans as the stretcher is put down, the blood-soaked bandage removed. No space for pity or horror. He isn't a man; he is a patient. Position the equipment above his ruined shoulder. Focus it. An image appears on the screen beneath the patient. There! A bullet lodged deep in the wound.

The surgeon nods and sets to work. Beads of sweat stand out on the patient's brow. He clenches his fists. Slowly, slowly, the surgeon draws out the bullet. It is over. Marie lets out a breath and feels her body relax.

Marie set up twenty mobile X-ray units (left) and two hundred fixed X-ray centres. In total, these treated more than one million injured soldiers.

A New World

11ᵀᴴ NOVEMBER 1918 Carefully, Marie attached the minute, fragile glass tube to the pump and flipped the switch to start the gas flow. A whirr, a tiny hiss, then BANG! Marie jumped, and the delicate tube flew from her fingers and smashed on the ground.

Surely that was a gun shot! Marie dashed to the window. A crowd was gathered in the street below, cheering and waving French flags. With a whoop, a man pointed his gun to the sky and fired again. Marie clapped her hands to her mouth and gasped.

"Marthe!" she shouted to her friend, working in the room next door, "The war is over! Stop your work at once — we must celebrate!"

Radium gives off a gas called radon. Marie captured this gas in tiny tubes and sent it to hospitals, where it was used to treat infected wounds.

20ᵀᴴ MAY 1921 Marie gazed wide-eyed around the ornate room in the White House, into which politicians and scientists were crammed like sardines. It was a year since an American journalist, Mrs Meloney, had visited her. Marie still remembered her look of shock when she learned that Marie had only one gram of radium — enough to draw off gas, but not enough to do any research.

Mrs Meloney raised money to buy Marie another gram of radium.

Marie had been in the USA for several weeks now. She had been amazed by her reception there — the cheering crowds, the parades, people giving her flowers. It had been an experience, but she would be relieved to go home, back to her laboratory.

The thought of work calmed her, so that she barely shook as the president stepped forward, hung a tiny golden key around her neck and handed her a small box with a golden lock.

"In testimony of the affection of the American people... I have been commissioned to present to you this little phial of radium."

Marie with President Warren Harding in 1921.

© GL Archive / Alamy

The Long Day Closes

MAY 1934 Wearily, Marie looked up from her test tube and rubbed her eyes. She had become used to her tiredness and the burns on her hands, but today she was struggling to focus. She staggered, and grabbed hold of the table to steady herself. Just a little fever... she would go home, rest... she would be fine by the morning.

4TH JULY 1934 Marie slept fitfully, gripped by fragments of dreams. At her side, her daughter Eve gently stroked her icy hand and smoothed the hair from her face. As the sun reached long, blood-red fingers through the curtains, Marie slipped quietly from the world, her long toil finally over.

*Marie Curie died of **aplastic anaemia (ay-plastic an-eem-ia)**, brought on by long exposure to radiation.*

Radioactivity — A Mixed Blessing

When the Curies accepted their Nobel Prize in 1903, they predicted that, as well as providing great benefits to mankind, radioactivity could do great harm. They were right.

Radiation is very useful in treating cancer, and has saved many lives. It destroys tumours, so some patients do not have to undergo surgery. Unfortunately, it also kills healthy cells, so it can make patients feel ill — many report symptoms such as sickness and headaches.

Scientists have found a way to produce electricity from radiation. With fuels like coal and oil in short supply, this could keep our lights and TVs running in the future. On the downside, accidents at power plants can release high levels of radiation. This can cause illness or death for people in the area. Areas around accident sites may be uninhabitable for years.

An abandoned school near to where a power plant exploded in 1986.

Food can be treated with radiation to make it last.

Radiation can also be used to kill mould and germs on food, which makes it last longer. This helps prevent food being wasted. However, some people believe that exposing food to radiation may cause health problems for people who eat it, while others argue that it ruins its flavour.

Radioactivity has lots of uses — it can help cure illness, power our homes and preserve our food. However, it also has negative impacts — it can make us ill, drive us from our homes and possibly ruin our food. Does the benefit outweigh the harm? There is no easy answer.

An Unexpected Honour

20TH APRIL 1995 The pale spring sun gleamed in a hazy sky, lending the faces of the assembled crowd a silvery sheen. A hush fell upon the crowd as twelve soldiers, bearing two wooden coffins, walked slowly along the stretch of white carpet towards the magnificent building.

"Mum," a small child whispered, "what's happening?"

"We've come to pay our respects to two great scientists," the child's mother murmured back. "Marie Curie is the first woman ever to be honoured for her work by being buried here. She worked so hard, for so long, to understand radioactivity and how it could help people. She didn't want fame or money, she just wanted to understand."

The Curies' remains were moved from a cemetery in southern Paris to the Panthéon (Panth-ee-un) — a building where some of the most important people in France are buried.

Nodding, the child cast the flower she was holding into the path of the oncoming coffin bearers. Taking her mother's hand, she frowned, then solemnly declared, "When I grow up, I'm going to be a scientist just like Marie Curie."

Glossary

aplastic anaemia — A disease which stops the body producing blood properly

cancer — A disease where unhealthy cells multiply and spread faster than healthy cells

chemical element — A substance made up of one type of atom, e.g. oxygen or gold

front line — The line of defence closest to the enemy army, where fighting takes place

governess — A woman who is employed to teach the children of one family

Nobel Prize — An international award given for very important work

Russian Empire — A large area that was controlled by Russia

thesis — A big piece of original research carried out by a student

tuberculosis — A serious disease, most often affecting the lungs

ASR21